THE TRIALS OF WELLS HARBOUR

THE TRIALS OF WELLS HARBOUR

John Barney

Mintaka Books

Published in the year two thousand by
Mintaka Books
30, Friars Quay, Norwich, Norfolk, NR3 1ES.
Tel 01603 612815
Fax 01603 614667

Origination, printing and binding by Witley Press Limited, Hunstanton, Norfolk, PE36 6AD.

British Library Cataloguing in Publication Data.
A catalogue record for this book is available from the British Library.

ISBN 0 95378 090 2

Contents

Abbreviations

Norfolk Record Office	NRO
Public Record Office	PRO

Acknowledgments

My interest in the history of Wells harbour came partly from earlier work on King's Lynn and its harbour in the eighteenth century, where some of the same characters appeared, and partly through attending John Dominy's course on *Changes in the Coastline of East Anglia*. My thanks are due to him; to Mr G.B. Walker, harbourmaster at Wells, and his staff for current information and access to the Commissioners' archive of records; to the staff of the Norfolk Record Office who hold copies of the engineers' reports and much other relevant matter; to photographers Derek Edwards of the Norfolk Air Photographs Library who took the aerial views and Terry Burchell who photographed the maps; and to Ian O'Brien who read the manuscript and who provided from his collection the original of the Ordnance Survey first edition.

Illustrations and maps

Aerial views

All aerial photographs reproduced by permission of Norfolk Air Photographs Library of the Norfolk Museums Service and the photographer Derek A. Edwards.

1. Origins

The first view of the harbour seen by most visitors to Wells is from the quayside or from the long embankment stretching out to the lifeboat house, the beach and the distant dunes of Holkham Meals. There is the inner channel, either wide at high water or a narrow snake winding around sands at low tide, and broad acres of saltmarsh away to the east. At the quay lie perhaps a few fishing craft and scattered near the channel, or more thickly in the main marsh creek, some dozens of yachts on moorings, few remaining afloat at low water. When the tide is out the view from the pathway across the dunes to the beach stretches across seeming miles of sands to the surf line in the far distance. The outer channel can then be crossed on foot.

The first view from seawards, these days almost invariably seen from the cockpit of a yacht, is rather more dramatic, being edged with tension. The navigator's first task, while still in deep water, is to find the Fairway buoy, not always easy against the background of dunes and trees which screen any view of the town itself, still well over two miles away, for until this buoy is located it is unwise in the extreme to stand in too close to the low-lying coast. The Fairway buoy is lit nowadays, but it would be a rash skipper who planned his first entrance to Wells in the dark or with anything more than a mild degree of north in the wind for the waves soon begin to break in the shoaling water near the bar. Locals familiar with the entrance and its hazards may enter in more difficult conditions but must never allow their familiarity to verge on contempt.

The channel inwards from the Fairway buoy is buoyed and lit, varying in direction from year to year, but is in fact little more than the best route inwards over the open beach. An inward bound vessel is totally exposed to any following sea until the route turns for a while alongshore close to the bathing beach, gaining then some protection from the higher sands to seaward. Sailing directions warn against trying an entrance earlier than two hours before high water even at spring tides. A boat entering before this runs a strong risk of striking the sand which in bad conditions could cause her to broach sideways to a following sea and be rolled over. Conditions become especially treacherous on the ebb if a wind is blowing onto the bar. As one pilot book states, "In sterner weather there can be nothing more productive of adrenaline than passing through the curling white water of the bar and reaching the sanctuary of the harbour behind the east sand."[1]

Once around the pinewood corner near the lifeboat house, where the channel takes a severely sharp bend, your craft enters the inner channel in sudden peace with a view of the town and quayside now less than a mile ahead. Care still needs to be paid to pilotage as the deepest water is seldom on a direct line to the quay but there are buoys and beacons to give guidance and grounding, though embarrassing, is unlikely to be fatal. This is the harbour as it is today, devoid of any commercial traffic beyond a little fishing, and increasingly devoted to leisure boating and sailing.

It was not always thus—ten thousand years ago it did not exist. There can be few harbours in the British Isles which do not owe their present shape and depth in some way to the huge rise in sea level (over 100 metres) caused by the melting of glaciers following the end of the latest ice age.[2] This applies as much to the tidal harbours of the north Norfolk coast as to the drowned valleys of the south and west. In the former case the sites of the present harbours were not even near the sea coast before the waters began their advance, the sea shore being north of the Dogger Bank and Britain joined to the Continent by a wide swath of land stretching from Yorkshire to the north of Denmark and from Sussex to Normandy. When the waters began their rise as the ice melted further north the advance of the shoreline southward across a gently shelving plain may have been—for a geological process—extremely rapid, reaching its present location about five thousand years ago. The ground thus flooded was covered with glacial till and much of this would have been effectively bulldozed forward as the shoreline moved inland producing shingle banks and accumulations of sand along and near the Norfolk coast.

This initial rise is thought to have brought the sea level by the Neolithic Age to as much as two metres above the present level. Thus the high tide line at Wells would have run just below the present five metre contour. Starting from the west the line would have been roughly along the old Holkham road (the B1105) to the site of the present town, then curving sharply in an exaggerated 'S' around the Northfield area, back to near the church, and then back again in another sharp curve to the east and finally in a wide sweep south of all the now drained marshland up to Halfway House on the Stiffkey Road before returning northwestward to the present high water coastline at the Nass promontory about 500 metres to the east of the town site. The relative sea level is believed to have fallen back in the Bronze Age by as much as four or five metres, risen by about the same amount in the Iron Age and early Roman period, fallen again by perhaps three metres in the early Medieval period, before rising gradually by about a metre or more to its present state.[3] These latter fluctuations may seem relatively small and their precise causes are not fully understood but they are probably important in the context of the formation of Wells harbour. Major questions remain: how and

MAP 1

Map of Wells harbour made in 1780 by Mr Biederman under the direction of engineer Robert Milne, with an amendment of 1781, reorientated to show true north at the top of the page. The early shoreline before any marshes were drained can clearly be seen.

This map was one of two made to illustrate Milne's report of 27 April 1781 to the attorneys acting for the executors of Sir John Turner. In his report of 4 May 1782 engineer John Smeaton referred specifically to this map, naming two features not found on later maps.

Joseph Hodskinson, in his report of 5 July 1782, criticised this map in certain particulars, most importantly in maintaining that the tidal meeting point drawn at the east side of the East Marsh was too far to seaward and that more water ebbed eastward than this map implied.

Approximate scale as reproduced here: 2 inches to 1 mile. Taken from an original in the Norfolk Record Office, MS486.

when did the dunes first form and did this/must this have preceded the formation of the saltmarsh?

The dunes are in fact barrier islands similar to the Frisian islands which are found to seawards of the shallow Waddenzee along the Frisian coast, though on a smaller scale. These Dutch and German islands are simply very large areas of sand with massive dunes on their seaward shore. Barrier islands are thought to form in a number of different ways, two of which seem possibilities at Wells.[4] Less likely, given the knowledge of the gradual if erratic extension of that point westward in historic times, is that the Wells dunes were once an extension of Blakeney Point. They may however have formed part of a similar spit which was breached by storm waves. More probable is that they originated as one or more sandbars following some minor retreat of the sea from the higher shoreline at and around Wells and subsequently kept their heads above water despite occasional storm damage, becoming viable dune islands before the water next rose. This suggests that the dune line formed at least one thousand years ago to fall within the last known period when the sea level was measurably below the present. Dunes need plenty of material to survive for which the gently sloping beach to seaward at Wells provides an adequate source. The same beach also serves as an absorber of wave energy to give some protection to the dunes even at high water.

Saltmarsh forms when silt laden seawater hesitates and then falls back at the top of each spring tide. In those conditions and when the shore is gently sloping the silt in suspension precipitates for a brief period when the water is near to stationary. Neap tides will not reach the deposited silt to wash it off, and the process will be repeated again at the next springs. Regular destructive waves are fatal to saltmarsh formation. This is why it needs either a very long beach to absorb wave energy or else a protective spit or barrier to form the edge of a lagoon and hence to keep large waves away altogether. Once some vegetation has formed on the silt the plants themselves act to filter silt out of the water and so increase the rate of deposition.[5] North Sea water has an unusual concentration of silt, especially near the eastern English coast and above all in the area near the Wash, probably derived mainly from wave-induced reworking of glacial deposits on the sea floor. Tide streams near the entrance to the Wash are rotatory, with the latter part of the flood stream setting east, out of the Wash itself and along the Norfolk north coast.[6] There should be plenty of silt in Wells water at the top of the tide. By the time of the earliest maps (c.1780) both the Holkham and Warham shores were lined with saltmarsh stretching seaward a mile or more.

Analysis of muds in the Warham marshes suggests some were laid down at least a thousand years ago[7]. If so, and if the dunes were necessary to protect the growing marsh, they must be even older. But saltmarsh without a protective barrier rising above spring tides is not infrequent. Examples include the inshore strips between the Elbe and the Weser in Germany and between the Crouch and the Blackwater in Essex. Nearer to Wells are the marshes of the Wash and those off Thornham. And much nearer still are the eastern parts of the Warham saltmarsh and the whole of the marshes opposite Stiffkey. In each of these examples a very wide area of either sand or mud stretches offshore from the marsh and these areas alone may have been sufficient to absorb enough wave energy to permit saltmarsh to form. However, even though those areas near Wells have no barrier now, they may have had one once. Faden's 1797 map of Norfolk (Map 3) shows what are either incipient dunes or at least substantial sand bars near to the low tide mark stretching from near Wells harbour entrance to east of Stiffkey. Current Ordnance Survey maps show a raised area, the High Sand, at the eastward end of this line, although this is certainly covered at high tide. Thus it is possible that the saltmarsh off Wells developed before the dunes although more probable that the dunes existed first if only in the form of sandbars covered at high water but still providing some protection to the growing marsh.

In the early and middle stages of the life of a salt marsh numerous small gullies are carved in the mud as the water from high tides runs off the marsh. These gullies tend to join at the lower levels of the marsh and form larger channels or creeks. On open coast the creeks may be numerous, each with its own exit to seawards, but at Wells all, excepting only those to the extreme east and west of the marshes, eventually coalesced into a single channel at the gap in the dunes. Flood tides bring silt into the creeks themselves as well as to the marsh surface, but a sufficient strength of ebb tide, especially as the water level falls, should scour away most of this. Nevertheless, in the long term and as the marsh rises and carries less water even at spring tides, there is a tendency for the creeks themselves to fill with silt. Such silting may be reduced or totally eliminated by land water coming down from rivers and streams and keeping a regular seaward flow of water at low tide, but Wells has no such advantage.[8] If the creeks are to remain open it is important that the largest possible tidal flow is maintained. It was always of especial importance to encourage the maximum swift tidal flow past the town and quay, particularly near low water when it could do the greatest good in scouring the creek bed and so removing any silt which might have been deposited there.

NOTES

1 Henry Irving, *The Tidal Havens of the Wash and Humber* (St Ives, 1983) p.10.

2 John Pethick, *An Introduction to Coastal Geomorphology*, (London, 1984) p.214. Strictly speaking we should refer to relative sea level. When northern Britain was depressed into the earth's mantle by massive weights of ice the southern half rose upwards in reaction. Once the ice melted an opposite effect set in which still continues. The rate of sink for Norfolk is minute but even one millimetre a year would amount to ten metres in ten thousand years. So far as measurements can be made the rate has in fact been higher. See R.J.N. Devoy, "Analysis of the geological evidence for Holocene sea-level movements in southeast England", *Proceedings of the Geologists' Association* 93 (1982) pp.65-90; Ian Shennan, "Holocene crustal movements and sea-level changes in Great Britain", *Journal of Quaternary Science*, 4 (1) (1989) pp.77-89; and K. Lambeck, "Late Devensian and Holocene shorelines of the British Isles and North Sea from models of glacio-hydro-isostatic rebound", *Journal of the Geological Society*, London 152 (1995) pp.437-448.

3 Harry Godwin, *Fenland: its ancient past and uncertain future* (Cambridge, 1978) Chart of relative sea levels p.106. Measurements for the Fens may not be valid for the north Norfolk coast and indeed later measurements for locations in the Fens close to but different from those surveyed by Godwin have been found to vary somewhat from his. The process of change in relative sea levels is imperfectly understood but is known to be uneven in time and location and subject to temporary reversals in

direction, probably climate induced. See Ian Shennan, "Interpretation of Flandrian sea-level data from the Fenland, England", *Proceedings of the Geologists' Association* 93 (1982) pp.53-63.

4 M.L. Schwartz, "The Multiple Causality of Barrier Islands" in M.L. Schwarz (ed.) *Barrier Islands*, (Stroudsberg, Penn, 1973).

5 Pethick, *Coastal Geomorphology*, Chapter 8.

6 Irving, *Tidal Havens*, tidal charts pp.64/5.

7 R.L Jefferies, "The North Norfolk Coast" in *Nature in Norfolk* (Norwich 1976) p.130.

8 It has been persuasively argued by John Dominy that before the last incursion of ice onto the present north Norfolk coast the Stiffkey Brook reached the sea via Wells, only cutting its present course via Stiffkey when blocked by ice.

2. Early history

Wells is known as a harbour from medieval times, the first references dating from the thirteenth century at which period the haven for the small ships of the time may have been as far up the main creek as the present Church Marsh. Nothing survives which could measure its importance until the sixteenth century when a record of 1580 lists 19 ships belonging there of over 16 tons, a total similar to the nearby ports of Cley and Blakeney but well below those for Yarmouth and King's Lynn.[1] Throughout the seventeenth century the Customs port books show the harbour, which was then designated a subdivision or "creek" of the port of King's Lynn, as busy on a moderate scale, importing predominately coal plus some salt, and exporting mainly grain, including malt, and smaller quantities of salt fish. As with all eastern coastal ports at that time ships came occasionally from London, the Netherlands or nearer ports bringing small quantities of every type of item or commodity, the grocery and hardware trades of the day.[2] Like other harbours along the north Norfolk coast such as Cley or Thornham, the volume of trade through Wells was limited by the nature of its immediate hinterland which was agricultural and not especially prosperous at a time when goods transport inland was limited to horsedrawn carts.

The principal trades of the town itself were fishing and malt production. Fishing vessels from Wells regularly worked north to Scotland and were amongst the numerous English vessels which fished Icelandic waters from the fifteenth to the end of the seventeenth century. Cod and other fish caught by Wells fishermen and salted at sea exceeded the capacity of local markets so that some was taken directly or by re-export to London or the south. In the early part and middle of the eighteenth century malt production from the barley grown in the area grew dramatically and Wells became the second (after Yarmouth) malt exporting port of the country. There are no figures for malt exported coastwise— there may have been but little—but shipments abroad of barley and malt from Wells in the years from 1744 to 1763, the great years of English grain exportation, averaged annually nearly ten thousand tons.[3]

A stone quay had been built close to the position of the present quay before 1662 when a petition from merchants and mariners of the town refer to it as being in disrepair. The petition asked Parliament to authorise the raising of finance to repair the quay and maintain the harbour, a prayer answered with the first Wells Harbour Act of 1663. This legislation allowed the levying of a charge on cargoes loaded or unloaded in the port and specified how these charges should be collected and applied by two persons elected by the merchants and shipowners of the port (whose appointments were to be confirmed by local magistrates). A further levy was authorised to finance a haven master whose duties were to lay buoys and erect beacons for the guidance of mariners.[4]

The late seventeenth and especially the eighteenth centuries were a great age of agricultural improvement. The lords of the manors adjacent to the coast became eager to acquire more land by the draining of saltmarsh, and none more so than the Coke family of Holkham. The marshes surrounding Holkham creek were enclosed by embankments late in the seventeenth century, extinguishing as any form of harbour that of Holkham which formerly had two exits to the sea via the present Holkham Gap and via the west fleet of Wells and through what is now the small lake at Abraham's Bosom to the main Wells channel. In 1719 there came a significant further intake of marsh when Thomas Coke, later first earl of Leicester and the builder of the great house at Holkham, enclosed by embankment a large area of land on the western side of Wells. Simultaneously adjacent land on the western side and another area to the east of the town were taken in by Sir Charles Turner who had acquired the Warham estate a few years before and had become lord of the manors of Wells and Warham. The western embankments can still be seen today.[5]

There is no record of objections by the town to these enclosures although hearsay evidence long after asserted that Sir Charles had promised that he would remove his eastern embankment if it proved to cause harm to the harbour. The loss of any saltmarsh must inevitably have reduced the area covered by high tides but it would seem that the loss on the western side may have had relatively little effect on the tidal scouring of the harbour as the exit of the ebb tide from that area did not pass the quay. Instead it first ran into the western fleet which in turn joined the main channel but well to seaward though inside the dunes. The loss of some of the eastern marsh was more significant as the ebb from here undoubtedly ran directly into the main harbour channel past the quay and thence to seaward contributing to the tidal scour at the most critical point for the clearance of deposited silt.

Some years after the raising of the new embankments both the harbour and an anchorage at the Pool began to silt up. This was put down to the loss of tidal run-off caused by the diminution of the area of saltmarsh flooded by the tide and consequent partial loss of tidal scour on the ebb. Consequently a Mr Freestone of Wells suggested and in 1749 had built a work opposite the town at the mouth of a large subsidiary creek, later known as Sluice Creek, which was designed to narrow its exit and so concentrate the flow of the ebb tide from a large part of the eastern marsh.

MAP 2

Map of Wells harbour dated 1782. Probably as surveyed in the spring of that year by Joseph Hodskinson and his assistants to illustrate his report of 5 July 1782. Reorientated to show true north at the top of the page.

Topographical differences from Map 1 are not significant but more emphasis is given to the Warham Slade marsh and the embankment which enclosed it. Also the alleged line of the old outer channel is emphasised and specifically related to the enclosure of Warham Slade.

This map has been much reproduced, in particular by the Tidal Harbours Commissioners in 1846 and more recently by Professor J. A. Steers, The Coastline of England and Wales (Cambridge, 1964).

Approximate scale as reproduced here: 2 inches to 1 mile. Taken from an original in the Norfolk Record Office, MS486.

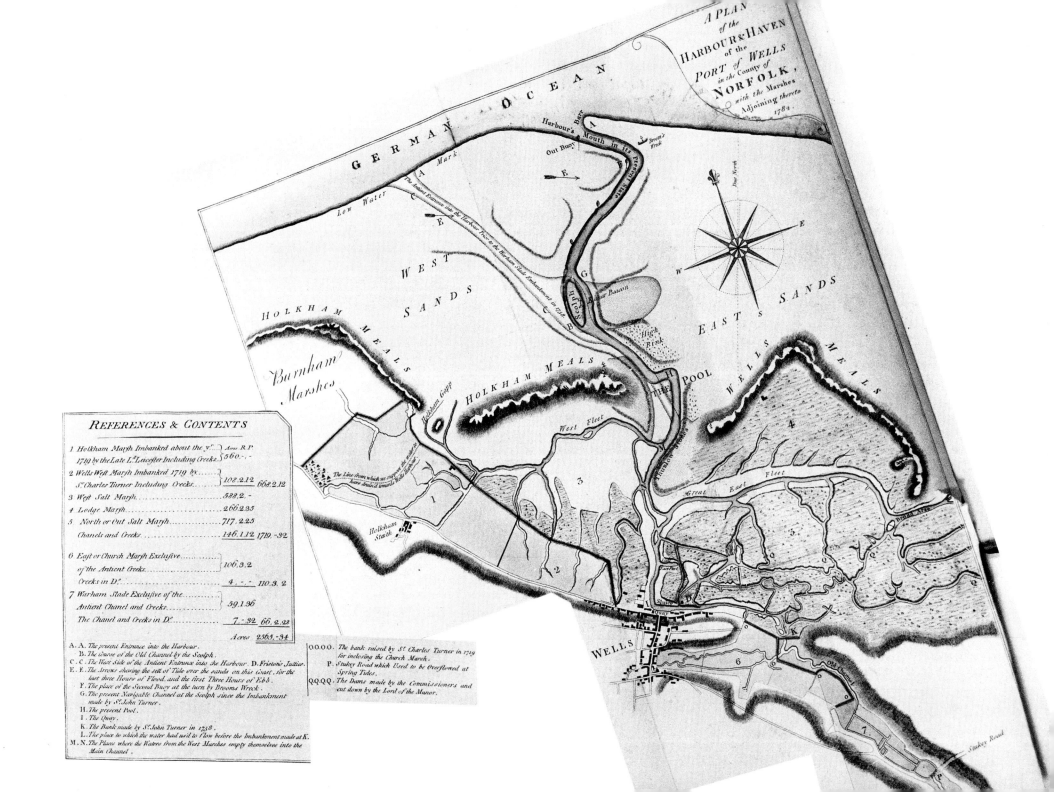

A PLAN of the HARBOUR & HAVEN of the PORT of WELLS in the County of NORFOLK, with the Marshes thereto Adjoining 1782

GERMAN OCEAN

Harbour's Mouth in its present State

Brown's Wreck

Out Buoy

Due North

WEST SANDS

EAST SANDS

WELLS MEALS

HOLKHAM MEALS

Burnham Marshes

HOLKHAM MEALS

The Line from which we suppose the water to have drained towards Wells Harbour

Scolph

Ballast Bacon

High Bank

THE POOL

West Fleet

East Fleet

Great

Holkham Gapp

Holkham Staith

WELLS

Stukey Road

Old Channel

REFERENCES & CONTENTS

	Acres R. P.	
1 Holkham Marsh Imbanked about the yr. 1719 by the Late Ld. Leicester Including Creeks	560. -. -	
2 Wells West Marsh Imbanked 1719 by Sr Charles Turner Including Creeks	102. 2. 12	662. 2. 12
3 West Salt Marsh	533. 2. -	
4 Lodge Marsh	266. 2. 35	
5 North or Out Salt Marsh	717. 2. 25	
Chanels and Creeks	146. 1. 12	1719. -. 32
6 East or Church Marsh Exclusive of the Antient Creeks	106. 3. 2	
Creeks in Do.	4. -. -	110. 3. 2
7 Warham Slade Exclusive of the Antient Chanel and Creeks	59. 1. 36	
The Chanel and Creeks in Do.	7. -. 32	66. 2. 28
	Acres	2565. -. 34

A.A. The present Entrance into the Harbour.
B. The Course of the Old Channel by the Scolph.
C.C. The West Side of the Antient Entrance into the Harbour. D. Friston's Justies.
E.E. The Arrows shewing the sett of Tide over the sands on this Coast, for the last three Hours of Flood, and the first Three Hours of Ebb.
F. The place of the Second Buoy at the turn by Brooms Wreck.
G. The present Navigable Channel at the Scolph since the Imbankment made by Sr John Turner.
H. The present Pool.
I. The Quay.
K. The Bank made by Sr John Turner in 1758.
L. The place to which the water had used to flow before the Imbankment made at K.
M.N. The Places where the Waters from the West Marshes empty themselves into the Main Channel.

O.O.O.O. The bank raised by Sr Charles Turner in 1719 for inclosing the Church Marsh.
P. Stukey Road which Used to be Overflowed at Spring Tides.
Q.Q.Q.Q. The Dams made by the Commissioners and cut down by the Lord of the Manor.

This work was said to have had a beneficial effect in scouring away the mud and sand that had built up in the harbour and channel from the mouth of the sluice down as far as the Pool. In 1758 another area on the eastern side, Warham Slade of some 66 acres, was embanked for draining by Sir Charles' nephew and heir Sir John Turner MP.[6] However by 1765 Freestone's sluice, having been originally constructed "in a slight manner" with facines, stakes, piles etc., had widened at its mouth to such an extent that it had become of little use. To reconstruct Freestone's sluice was likely to be expensive so that in 1769 a new Parliamentary Act was procured to enable finance to be raised. This Act established a self perpetuating body of commissioners to administer the harbour, provided the required borrowing powers, and established a new rate of harbour charges based on cargoes loaded and unloaded on the security of which finance could be raised.[7] The new commissioners then replaced the sluice on the same site with one better built than the original. This was for a time effective in clearing the channel but in 1777 was found to have been nearly destroyed by worms.[8]

The commissioners took advice from a Mr Wooler who advised a similar but entirely new construction in a somewhat different situation and with different materials. The cost was estimated at two thousand pounds which, being well in excess of the commissioners' uncommitted borrowing powers, was thought excessive and it was decided instead merely to repair the existing sluice. However the harbour continued to silt and by 1778 they resolved to take action to reopen the Warham Slade area which had been shut off in 1758, believing that this action must substantially enhance the tidal scour. They began by taking Counsel's opinion who advised that all the embankments which prevented the flow and reflow of the tides, stopped up the harbour, or were prejudicial to navigation, were nuisances at the time they were made…but that some had been there so long that there would be difficulty in getting them removed. He considered the best course would be to indict those persons who had made or continued the latest such bank, that is to say Sir John Turner. However Counsel considered that it would be dangerous simply to pull down the bank; better first to consult with Sir John to see if some accommodation could be found.[9]

The commissioners were a disparate body including not only merchants and shipowners of the town who would have the most interest in keeping the harbour open, but certain local landowners, two of whom were Thomas Coke of Holkham[10], heir to the Lord Leicester who had originally erected some of the banks, and Sir John himself. The latter was by now an ageing, obstinate and indolent man, no longer since 1774 MP for King's Lynn, and by 1779 heavily in debt with large mortgages on the Warham estate and having little other property. As with all requests made to him in his later years, his response to the demand to remove his embankment was one of delay and evasion. Although in 1779 his lawyers were putting forward possible compromises, later that year the commissioners went to the Norwich Assizes where the Grand Jury declared his bank a common nuisance and ordered it to be taken down.

It was not the case that the harbour had become totally unusable although some of the mariners were the strongest complainants. By now malt export had died away to near negligible amounts as had export of any kind (the country was in any case at war and privateers were making severe inroads on east coast shipping) but figures for coastal shipments of corn products from Wells, chiefly barley, show an average of 7,500 tons over the years 1781 to 1786 inclusive, and the port as ranking tenth in the country for such shipments.[11] While there are no figures for the import of coal at that time it is certain that such imports would have continued as they did, despite all hazards, for all east coast harbours throughout the century and well into the next. Moreover the principal complaint was not the silting up of the inner harbour and channel, although that was serious, but a shift in the alignment of the outer channel across the sands. Once more westerly in direction, it had been moving gradually to the east. Not more than twenty years before it had run north-west but had now come to lie north-east by east. As a result the entrance was much less safe than it had been when a ship with a "proper" wind could sail directly in on a flood tide which ran roughly in the direction of the channel. Now, once the water had risen above the western sands, the tide set across the channel making entrance without a strong leading wind much more dangerous as ships were driven over onto the eastern sands, and many had been lost.

NOTES

1 Arthur W Purchas, *Some History of Wells-next-the-Sea & District* (Ipswich, 1965) p.47.

2 PRO E190 435/7 & 438/7 port books for 1638/39 & 1679/80.

3 Of this malt was by far the greater part with a maximum of over 12,000 tons of malt alone in 1750. Two years, 1757 and 1758 when there was an embargo on any exports, are excluded from the average. The malt very largely went to the Dutch distilleries at Schiedam and Rotterdam. ADD MSS 38387 pp.31-52.

4 15 Chas II. The copy of the petition is at NRO FX 245/12/14.

5 Sir Charles Turner, Bart, was MP for King's Lynn from 1695 to his death in 1738. Making a fortune from the wine and other trades, the Turner family dominated Lynn politics from the late seventeenth to the mid eighteenth century. Sir Charles, who had married a sister of Sir Robert Walpole, Lynn's other MP, bought the Warham estate c. 1710 from the heirs to Admiral Sir Clowdeseley Shovell.

6 Sir John Turner, Bart, MP (1712/1780) inherited the Warham estate from his uncle and in succession to Sir Charles was MP for King's Lynn from 1738 to 1774.

7 Wells Harbour Act, 9 Geo III c.3 (1769). Both this and the Act of 1663 were repealed by a replacement Act 5&6 Wm IV c.48 (1835) and the latter Act was extended and altered by 7&8 Vict. c.93 (1844).

8 Case submitted to Serjeant Grose, 31 January 1778, annexed to Appendix to Second Report of Royal Commission on Tidal Harbours, pp. 437/466, section on Wells harbour. Also "Report on Wells Harbour", in *Reports of the late John Smeaton FRS*, Vol. III (London, 1812).

9 Tidal Harbours Commission appendix; Opinion of Serjeant Grose.

10 Thomas William Coke (1754/1842) MP, the famous agriculturist "Coke of Norfolk", a great-nephew of the first earl of Leicester.

11 S. Lambert (ed), *House of Commons Sessional Papers of the Eighteenth Century*, Vol 49 (Delaware, 1975) pp.211, 235-9.

3. The first trials[1]

Despite the Court ruling in the summer of 1779 that the bank must be removed Sir John took no action while the lawyers continued to temporise. Sir John had one friend amongst the commissioners, the rector of Wells, the Reverend Mr Robinson, who reported on the commissioners' meetings but was unable to sway the determination of the majority to have the bank taken down. Yet matters did not come to a head until after June 1780 when Sir John died intestate and insolvent. His heirs were his two daughters and administration of his estate was undertaken jointly by his sons-in-law Sir Martin Browne Folkes, Bart, and John Hales Esq.[2] These gentlemen were at once faced with the necessity of selling the Warham property, a task which was bound to be greatly impeded by the dispute over the bank. On the other side, alarmed by the possible delay which Turner's death might engender, the commissioners, having carried out a fresh inspection of the harbour which they thought in a worse state than ever, resolved in July to employ men to break down the bank after Michaelmas.

The commissioners' decision was reached despite a violent intervention in their debate by Coke who thought that there was a chance that their action would cause the old eastern banks to be overwhelmed. These banks, he said, had been taken in a short time after those at Holkham and he had never heard them complained of. If they were in fact injurious to the harbour then he was persuaded that his own embankments must be equally so: but until they were so proved he gave notice that if any attempt should be made to cut or destroy *his* banks, he would defend them in the same manner as if his house was attacked. To preserve the main eastern part of the drained marshes from destruction he wished they would allow time for rebuilding the older banks erected by Sir Charles Turner which had given no offence for nearly sixty years.[3]

Alarmed by the commissioners' resolution, Folkes and Hales, who had been advised that physical resistance to any attempt to break the bank would be lawful but less than wise, obtained an injunction from the Court of Chancery and themselves sued the commissioners. To assist them in their action their attorneys retained Robert Mylne[4], a professional engineer of some note, who attended at Wells in the Spring and commissioned maps by Mr Biederman, a local surveyor, which served as a basis for much of the later arguments (see Map 1). Mylne's report dated 28 April 1781, asserted that it was not the effect of the bank which was ruining the harbour but a consequence of material brought in by the tides.

The case was tried at the Norwich Assizes in early August 1781, the decision going in favour of the plaintiffs, Folkes and Hales. The report in the *Norwich Mercury* was meagre, merely noting the cause, the decision, the names of the judge and counsel for both sides, the fact that the trial was before a special jury, and that it extended over two days. If we can believe the highly tendentious report of the later retrial a year later (reproduced below) Mylne's evidence decided the case despite contradictory evidence from numerous pilots and mariners. It does not seem that his written report, in which he suggested that the material choking the harbour might be the product of rivers further to the east and north such as the Humber and Great Ouse, was before the jury, but he must at least have said this in oral evidence. However it is clear that he went further, perhaps as a result of cross examination, and suggested that the material was brought in due to "an opposite meeting of the tides between Flamborough Head and Foulness [off Cromer]." This was rash and can have been no more than speculation. It was to be seized on after the trial by the opposition.

Remarks made later by Lord Mansfield at a hearing in the Court of King's Bench at which the losers requested a retrial throw some further light on what had gone wrong. The hearing at the Assizes, which overall lasted for seventeen hours, had started early one morning but it was not until the early hours of the following day that Mylne was called to give evidence. Lord Mansfield was concerned that Mylne had at one point admitted that the latest bank must have caused some harm to the harbour, however minor, and that this admission might have decided the case in favour of the commissioners had he not then retracted this admission under further challenge. The defendants alleged that what Mylne had said constituted a theory entirely new to them and complained that their witnesses could not be recalled to consider it, let alone to rebut it. Their plea was accepted and a retrial was ordered to give them time to "examine the veracity" of Mylne's evidence. It was at this stage that other engineers were called in, John Smeaton[5] for the Turner estate, and Joseph Hodskinson and Joseph Nickalls[6] for the defendants, all of whom reported in the first half of 1782.

The Reverend Mr Robinson played host to Smeaton during the latter's flying visit in March, despite braving ostracism by his fellow commissioners. In a letter to Folkes he described Smeaton's energetic three days which involved marching the seawalls, measuring tidal depths from a moored boat, and riding furiously along the low tide shore of the outer sands as far as the entrance to Blakeney harbour, all amongst intermittent snowshowers. Robinson was much taken with Smeaton, remarking, "I never

MAP 3

Section of Faden's Map of Norfolk published in 1797, surveyed by Thomas Donald and Thomas Milne, 1790 to 1794. The harbour mouth of Wells is specifically dated October 1793 implying that the Wells survey was done at that time. This unique dating of one feature also suggests that the surveyors were well aware of its tendency to move. The entrance configuration is markedly different to that shown by Maps 1 and 2 of the 1780's.

The detailing of the marshes and channels is poor but the map at this scale is useful for showing the relationship of Wells harbour to the surrounding coast and to inland features. Note the long line of apparent sand bars close to the low water mark from near Wells harbour entrance continuing eastward to the harbours of Blakeney and Cley. Note also that T. W. Coke is shown as the proprietor of Warham Manor, formerly owned by Sir John Turner, as well as of his main seat at Holkham.

Scale here at slightly less than the original scale of 1 inch to 1 mile. Reproduced by permission of the Norfolk Record Society from their six sheet reproduction in Norfolk Record Society Volume 42.

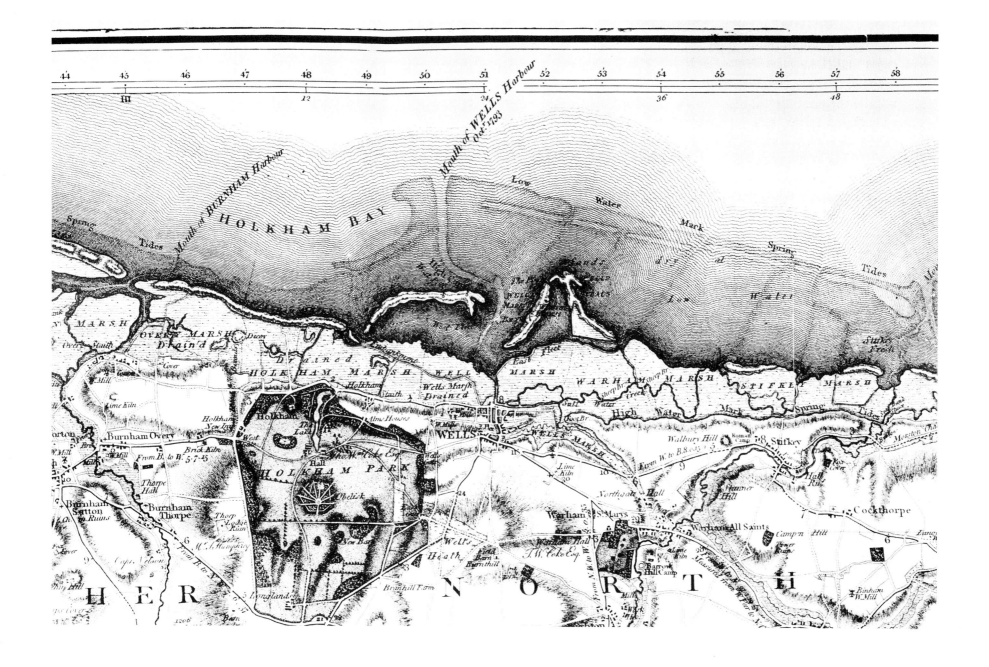

spent so many agreeable hours with so entertaining a man in my life." A few weeks later he reported scornfully that the rival team (Hodskinson was assisted by John Grundy and Thomas Hogard) had spent some ten days on site, so much time he felt being squandered solely to increase the expense.

All the new engineers produced written reports. Hodskinson, who submitted his own map (see Map 2), relied chiefly on discussions with pilots and on tidal measurements. It was common ground that the upper part of the harbour was dependent on the scour of the ebb tide to keep its channel open. Hodskinson argued that the area cut off by Sir John's bank, although relatively small, was uniquely valuable in providing scour because it stretched far inland and as a result had a significantly later high tide. Thus the ebb from this area must have begun later than from the rest of the saltmarsh and would have run faster and nearer to low water further down the harbour. Nickall's brief report merely seconded this and instanced a number of other tidal harbours in Britain which remained open despite having no permanent stream of landwater to flush away deposited silt. Much more speculatively Hodskinson went on to assert that it was particularly the ebb from Warham Slade which had served to keep the Pool at a good depth and to ensure that the outer channel continued to the north-west.

Smeaton's report, while in its conclusions similar to Mylne's, was considerably the more closely argued. He thought that the decline of the harbour had very likely begun long before and that its more recent acceleration was probably due to the enclosures earlier in the century which had been far larger than anything taken in by Sir John. He pointed out how gradual such changes tended to be in the absence of violent storms. He described how a tidal harbour might slowly construct itself as the saltmarsh gradually built up to the level of neap tides, requiring gullies to accommodate the run-off which would develop as creeks. Then, in the right conditions as had happened at Wells, the creeks, if constricted by obstructions such as the dunes, might join to form a considerable channel as the single exit of the entire tide from the area. However this same harbour would eventually destroy itself. The deposition of silt would slow as the marsh rose higher but would continue until the land grew to the level of the very highest tides. But the same process would gradually reduce the volume of run-off since the marsh would be covered less and less frequently. As this slowdown occurred the gullies would begin themselves to silt up from their inner ends and ultimately the creeks and the main channel itself would follow. Thus, lacking any intervention by man, a tidal harbour without any landwater running through was in the long run doomed.

It was not possible, he admitted, to say that the enclosure of some sixty acres by Sir John had no effect at all on the amount of water running out of the harbour, but sixty acres was a very small proportion of the whole. Moreover, although it might be true that the ebb had begun later at the head of the Slade and so the tide ran out from there somewhat nearer to the time of low water by the quay, he thought the Slade only filled with water on extreme tides and so could assist with scour only a few times each year. The loss of the land enclosed sixty years earlier would have had far more effect since the area was so much larger. The only solution must be engineering works to pen back water and discharge it at low tide as was done in several ports on the Continental shore.

He thought the action of a properly built and properly operated sluice would be far more effective than relying on the undirected tide alone.[7] As to the Pool he was pessimistic. Probably this had been filling for a long time with sand brought down by the west channel. There was a constant supply of sand off the back of the Holkham dunes. However great the scour engineered in the upper harbour it would not save the Pool which must eventually fill.

As regards the channel from the Pool to the sea he observed that the channel could move all too readily since it lay through "large broad open sands", which sand "…being perfectly clean, and free from particles that might create tenacity, when dried by the sun is capable of being blown by the wind, and moved by the common agitation of the sea, and very considerable changes are wrought by the action of the sea in great storms and tempests…" He understood that the distance from the Pool to low water mark was as great as it had ever been known "in man's memory", but that the available draught of water in this outer channel had not altered materially over the same period. The north Norfolk shore was the recipient, from whatever source, of a great deal of loose material, and the winds and tides would shape this to their fancy. He did not say the outer channel could not move back to the north-west but there was nothing men could do to influence it. Water would take the shortest course it could find that trended steadily down to the low tide level.

The second trial took place, again at Norwich Assizes, in late July 1782. The team of counsel for Folkes and Hales was the same as in the previous year, led by Henry Partridge, a barrister with strong Norfolk connections.[8] However the other side had brought up heavy artillery in the person of George Hardinge (1743/1816), barrister of the Middle Temple, solicitor-general to Queen Charlotte, occasional author, shortly to be counsel for the East India Company in opposition to Fox's India Bill of the following year, and a Tory MP. What is known of the trial comes entirely from the following report which was printed in identical terms in both the *Norwich Mercury* and its rival the *Norfolk Chronicle*. One cannot help feeling that the report, at least the second part, was inserted by a partisan of the harbour commissioners and perhaps, perish the thought, by Hardinge himself:

[Issue of 27 July] On Thursday morning at seven o'clock came on to be tried before Mr Justice Gould and a Special Jury the long contested action of trespass wherein Sir Martin Browne Folkes, Bart, and Robert Hales Esq…are plaintiffs and Geo. Chadd Esq and others, commissioners of the harbour of Wells, defendants. The Judge adjourned the Court at ten o'clock in the evening of Thursday, and early the next morning proceeded again on the trial which was not ended when this paper went to press. Two of the most eminent counsel in London are engaged in the business. An action for the same purpose was brought last summer assizes, by order of the Court of Chancery, to try whether a bank erected on the coast near the town of Wells, was a nuisance to the harbour, and after a trial of 17 hours a verdict was found in favour of the plaintiffs.

The following Gentlemen compose the Special Jury to try the above Cause:

> Sir John Berney of Kirby Bedon
> Francis Columbine of Thorp next Norwich
> Thomas Kerrick of Goldstone
> John Frere of Roydon
> John Kerrick of Redenhall with Harleston
> Robert Marham of Stratton Stawless
> Robert Croft of West Harling

Richard Wright of East Harling
Simon Rath of East Dereham
Horatio Hamond of Dersingham
James Smyth of East Dereham
Humphrey Repton of Sustead

[These were highly respectable gentleman although Sir John Berney later became insolvent. Thomas Kerrick had been High Sheriff of the county; John Frere became an MP for Norwich; John Kerrick became a volunteer colonel; Robert Marham appears as a country house owner on Faden's map of Norfolk; Horatio Hamond was a younger brother of Anthony Hamond of Westacre, one of Norfolk's principal landowners; and Humphrey Repton was the later famous landscape architect. It appears that they had visited Wells and viewed the bank at the end of June in preparation for the hearing.]
[Issue of 3 August] On Thursday the 25th of last month came to be tried before that able and upright Judge Sir Henry Gould and a most respectable and impartial Jury of Gentlemen the important cause between ...[as in previous issue and the question before the jury then recited]

The cause was first tried at Norwich Assizes 1781 when Mr Robert Mylne an engineer deposed (in contradiction to all other witnesses examined in the cause) that the bank was of no detriment to the harbour and he imputed its decay to other causes viz: to the operation of the ebb tides from the River Humber and Lynn Channel, and to the opposite meeting of tides between Flamborough Head and Foulness; whereupon the Jury relying on the weight of Mr Mylne's abilities and knowledge, and not having the least doubt of the truth of his evidence, found a verdict for the plaintiffs. This verdict was afterwards set aside by the Court of Kings Bench and a new trial ordered in order to enable the defendants to enquire into the truth or falsehood of Mr Mylne's testimony. Upon the second trial it was proved that the tides from the River Humber and Lynn Channel acted in quite contrary directions, and not towards the Wells harbour, and that there was no meeting of opposite tides between Flamborough Head and Foulness and that Wells harbour could not possibly have been affected by the causes assigned by Mylne who did not (for obvious reasons) venture to appear at the second trial to repeat and support the evidence which he had delivered at the first. The reports of the engineers from both sides were by agreement delivered to the Jury. Mr Mylne and Mr Smeaton in their reports entered into a scientific observation of the question and imputed the decay of the harbour to certain latent and imperceptible operations of nature which they said had been destroying this harbour for centuries past. The Court however rejected Mylne's and Smeaton's doctrines with the utmost disdain and considering the question as a plain and simple matter of fact, not imperceptible to but capable of being judged of by plain common sense, refused to balance the speculative doctrines, scientific opinions and visionary conjectures of Mr Mylne and Mr Smeaton, against direct and positive evidence of facts proved by a variety of mariners and other witnesses whose experience and observations had enabled them to point out the injury done to the harbour by the bank in question without referring to the latent operations of nature which were not perceptible to any human's understanding except those of Mr Mylne and Mr Smeaton.

The patience of the Judge and the indefatigable attention of the Jury in the course of the second trial which lasted for two days cannot be enough admired; and the general applause with which the verdict in favour of the defendants was received affords the strongest proof of the public satisfaction at finding that by the voice of the Jury the second harbour for the exportation of malt within the Kingdom of Great Britain was restored to the community.

The Counsel for the plaintiffs were Mr Partridge (whose abilities and conduct of his client's case certainly deserve great commendation) Mr Jodrell, Mr Wilson and Mr Sayer: Counsel for the defendants Mr Hardinge (Solicitor General to her Majesty) Mr Cole, Mr Grabon and Mr Jones.

It would be unjust to pass over in silence the uncommon abilities and judgement which Mr Hardinge displayed in the course of this important trial; his vast and astonishing powers of elocution; his indefatigable attention and his uncommon exertion in support of his clients' cause, could only be excelled by his singular and disinterested behaviour in refusing to accept a larger fee than 100 guineas when the sum of 300 guineas was offered him.

N.B. It is a debt due to common justice to say that the verdict given on the second trial cannot in any view be considered a reflection on the Jury upon the first because it is notorious that the evidence which the Jury on the first trial founded their verdict was on the second contradicted and clearly proved to be erroneous.

Thus, however much Smeaton's report had correctly identified the problems and the only solutions which were ever even partially adopted, the commissioners had won the day, a triumph of Norfolk conservatism over what were described as the mere opinions of scientific men, foreigners to the county, who lacked any understanding of "facts" known to the local practical men. Yet the point on which the case seems to have turned, the source of the accumulating material, was not really an issue, Smeaton observing in his report that, whatever the cause, much had arrived and more continued to do so.

1 Copies of the various engineers' reports, certain maps, and notes, and copy court and press reports on the progress of the successive legal actions are in the Norfolk Record Office under reference MS486. The originals of the press reports can be found in the *Norwich Mercury*. Certain letters in the Folkes of Hillington estate correspondence, NRO MC50, also refer to the suits, in particular 27/5,6,7 & 9; 29/2.2 & 8; 33/14 & 16 and also NRO NRS 8723 and 8730.

2 Sir Martin Browne Folkes of Hillington (1749/1821) MP for King's Lynn from 1790 until his death. John Hales was the Collector of Customs at Lynn. A minor but embarrassing discovery which they made was that Sir John had been (inadequately) supporting two illegitimate daughters apprenticed to a milliner in Lincoln.

3 NRO MC50 29/8.

4 Robert Mylne (1734/1811) engineered, inter alia, Blackfriars Bridge in London.

5 John Smeaton (1724/1792) was perhaps the most respected engineer in the country at that time. His most famous work in a highly varied career was the third Eddystone lighthouse.

6 Neither Hodskinson nor Nickalls obtained the eminence of Mylne or Smeaton but both were well known in their day. Interestingly both supplied opinions for the borough of King's Lynn ten years later in support of that town's opposition to the proposed Eau Brink Cut to shorten the River Ouse while Mylne was retained by the proposers of the scheme. Hodskinson practised in Clerkenwell and was best known as a surveyor and mapmaker. (see Gregory Tonkin, "Expert Advice", *East Anglian Magazine*, June 1981, pp. 380/1). He was the surveyor of a well known map of Suffolk.

7 The various editions of the sluice appear none of them to have been more than a means of constricting the entrance to the middle marsh creek to maximise the velocity of the flow through it. Smeaton would have liked a much more substantial structure which actually impounded the marsh water at high tide and discharged it under control shortly before low water to provide a hosepipe effect applied to the harbour bottom.

8 It is not clear if this was the Henry Partridge of Northwold who served as recorder of King's Lynn from 1745 for some twenty years or he who was recorder of Norwich from 1788 or whether these were one and the same man. Rye, *Norfolk Families* (Norwich, 1913) gives only one person, a King's Counsel, born 1711 and dying 1793, but if this is correct he would have been nearly seventy at the date of the first trial.

4. The final trial and aftermath

The reports of the engineers had been made available to the jury at the second trial but the engineers had not been called upon to give oral evidence or to be cross examined. This may have been a tactical ploy by the plaintiffs as regards Mylne in view of his gaffe at the first trial; it is not even clear that he attended the trial, but they certainly had wanted Smeaton to be called, especially as he intended to bring additional evidence by comparing Wells with other north Norfolk tidal harbours. Smeaton had been informed by his guide across the sands that Blakeney harbour entrance had moved half a mile eastward in recent years and he had wished to use this to show that Wells' entrance was not unique in its wanderings. The refusal by the judge to allow Smeaton to be called was used as the basis for an application to the Court of King's Bench by Folkes and Hales for a further retrial.

Their successful application was reported in the *Norwich Mercury* on 30 November 1782. Perhaps this time the reporter was a friend of the applicants as it was noted that the Court had "unanimously disapproved of the rejecting of the evidence abovementioned, declaring the whole question to be a matter of scientific opinion, incapable of being properly discussed without the evidence of men of science, conversant in the nature of harbours". Moreover, "Lord Mansfield passed high encomiums on the consumate skill and integrity of Mr Smeaton who had on several occasions been examined in causes of a similar nature tried before his lordship". This paragraph, and a poorly informed letter to the paper a week later by "A.B." who thought the circumstances of Yarmouth might be adduced to throw some light on the changes at Wells, brought forth a letter to the paper on 14 December (printed also in the *Norfolk Chronicle*) castigating AB for daring to express any opinion on a matter which was to be retried and the author of the original paragraph for repeating Lord Mansfield's remarks on Smeaton. This author signed himself A.B.C. but from his verbatim repetition of much of the report on the second trial can probably be identified as the author of that as well. However he went further than that report and his sarcasm was withering.

Referring to the judge's refusal to hear evidence concerning other tidal harbours he wrote:

> ...the Judge, upon being appealed to, sustained the Objection, declaring that such Evidence might lead to an hundred Enquiries into the circumstances of other Harbours, and create an hundred different Issues.

> At last appeared the great, the skilful, the celebrated, the omniscient Mr Smeaton, with a view of giving his Opinion upon the Evidence of the other Witnesses, and of assigning by his Opinion and "Conjectures" other Causes of the Decay of the Harbour, besides and exclusive of the Cause proved by the Commissioners.

> The Council [sic] for the Commissioners, knowing that the Jury had been in possession of Mr Smeaton's Report for upwards of a Week were desirous, if possible, to save themselves the trouble of having it repeated in Court, and therefore (and for no other Reason whatever) they endeavoured to shorten the Trial (which had lasted near two Days) by insisting that, unless Mr Smeaton's Opinion

was founded upon Facts, within his own knowledge, he ought not to be permitted to speak upon a mere Matter of "Opinion" alone…"

The third trial which was held, again at Norwich Assizes, in August 1783 before yet another special jury appears to have been an exceptionally vituperative affair although perhaps shorter in duration than its predecessors. This time the plaintiffs brought in a more senior barrister to head their team, Sir James Mansfield then solicitor general to the government.[1] The reports dated 30 August in the two Norfolk papers are again identical and from the phraseology are almost certainly from the pen of the previous reporter who refers to the case as one of the most important which had ever been tried in the county. Thus:

[the commissioners proved that] until the Erection of the Bank the Harbour was the safest and best Harbour on the north coast of the County…that no Ships or Lives were ever lost within the Harbour previous to the erection of the Bank…that divers Ships and Cargoes and numberless Lives have been lost between the Pool and the Bar since 1758…

From [Mylne, who did appear, and Smeaton] the Jury heard wild Conjectures, extravagant Assumptions and unintelligible Opinions without any FACTS…One of these Gentlemen called himself a JURYMAN, the other a WITNESS but both seemed to think that their Sentiments were to decide the Cause.

A singular Letter being produced in Court under

MAP 4

Section of the 1st edition of the Ordnance Survey (Sheet 68–NW portion) published in 1838 from an original survey of 1815/16. However the detail below high water mark would have been taken from later Admiralty surveys and includes certain features, such as a lifeboat house and various banks on the East Marsh, which were not present at the time of the original survey. The first lifeboat house was built in 1830.

The detailing of the creeks and marshes is superior to Map 3 (Faden's). Note that the harbour entrance has changed once again. It would seem that by the time of the survey Coke's new embankment to close off Warham Slade had been constructed although it is placed further inland than Sir John Turner's 1759 bank.

Scale here reproduced is at approximately 2 inches to 1 mile: original is at 1 inch to 1 mile. From a copy in possession of Ian O'Brien. See also the larger section at 1 inch to 1 mile reproduced on the front cover.

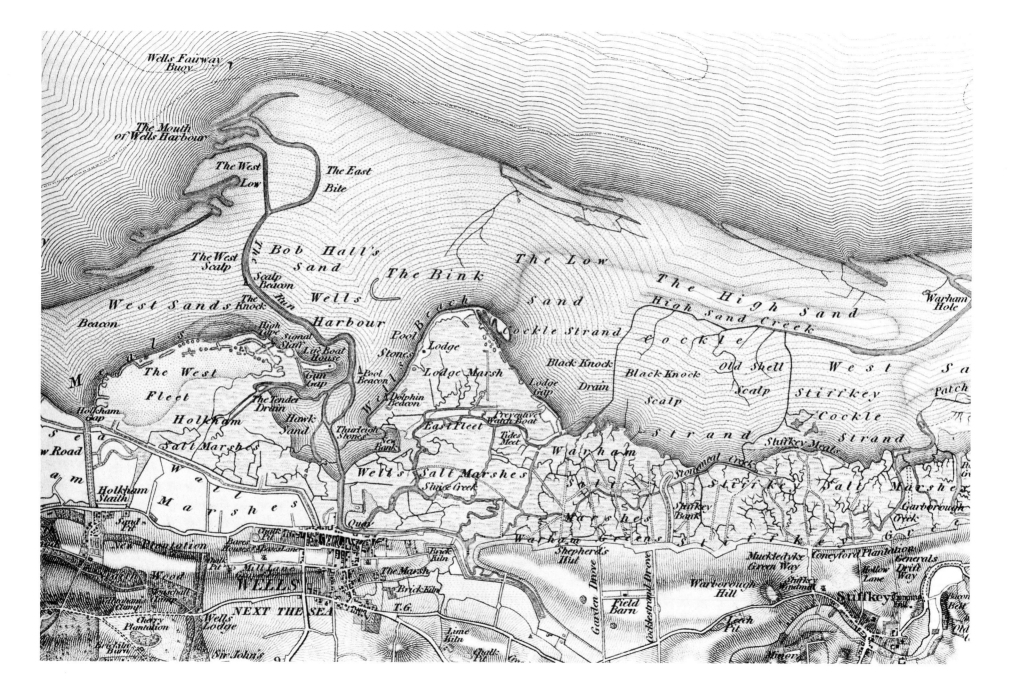

Wells Fairway
Buoy

The Mouth
of Wells Harbour

The West
Low

The East
Bite

The West
Scalp

Bob Hall's
Sand

The Bink

The Low

The High Sand

Warham
Hole

Scalp
Beacon

Wells

Sand

High Sand Creek

West Sands

The Knock

Run

Harbour

Beach

Cockle Strand

Cockle

Beacon

High Cape Signal
Staff

Life Boat
House

Pool
Stones

Lodge

Black Knock

Old Shell

West

The West

Gun
Gap

Pool
Beacon

Lodge Marsh

Black Knock

Scalp

Stiffkey

Patch

Fleet

The Tender
Drain

Hawk
Sand

Dolphin
Beacon

Lodge
Gap

Drain

Scalp

Cockle

Holkham
Gap

Holkham
Salt Marshes

Thurleigh
Stones

New
Banks

East Fleet

Prevenaye
Watch Boat

Tide
Meet

Strand

Strand

Stiffkey Meals

Sea

w Road

am

Holkham
Staith

Warham
Salt
Marshes

Warham

Salt

Marshes

Stonemeal Creek

Stiffkey
Bank

Stiffkey

Salt

Marshes

Garborough
Creek

Marshes

Wells Salt Marshes

Sluice Creek

Quay

Warham Greens

Stiffkey

New Plantation

Sand Pit

Brick Kiln

Shepherd's
Hut

Garden Drove

Muckledyke
Green Way

Coneyford Plantation

Generals
Drift
Way

Patch

Wood

WELLS

The Marsh

Brick Kiln

Field
Barn

Warborough
Hill

Stiffkey
Windmill

Hollow
Lane

STIFFKEY

Cherry
Plantation

Wells
Lodge

NEXT THE SEA

T.G.

Cocklestrand Drove

Leech
Pit

Lime
Kiln

Smeaton's hand, the defendant's Counsel did not give him the Credit of asking him a single Question on the Merits of the Cause.

Some idea of the quality of the debate can be gained from a published exchange of correspondence a year later between Mylne and Hardinge which ended with a grudging public apology by the latter to Mylne for doubting his good faith in court and "menacing him with a threat to indict him for perjury".[2]

The jury's decision was for the commissioners but contained an important rider, reading:

> The Jury agrees that the continuance of the Bank is in some Degree of Injury to the Harbour but are not all agreed to it's being a material Injury, and that it did not appear to the Jury from the Evidence that any legal Proceedings were had within the Space of twenty Years from the time of the erection of the Bank.[3]

Only four of the jurors were for the words underlined. Nevertheless, as might have been expected from these litigants, the wording of the decision was seized upon by the lawyers for Folkes and Hales as an opportunity for a new hearing before the King's Bench. Here they sought to have the verdict entered as in their favour, but after lengthy arguments by counsel and long speeches by the judges they were turned down and ordered to pay costs which were ultimately assessed as amounting to five hundred and sixty-two pounds.[4]

Early in 1784 a letter refers to Folkes and Hales applying for more time to complete their own bank before the commissioners started to cut through the old one. Later in the year they sold the whole Warham estate, which included the marshes, to Thomas Coke for just under fifty-eight thousand pounds, a sum more than sufficient to discharge old Sir John's accumulated debts.[5] It would appear that the loss of the Slade drained marsh had reduced the price by approximately two thousand pounds. Coke's combined estates now surrounded Wells on its landward side.

Perhaps the removal of the bank provided some temporary improvement to the harbour but thirty-five years later, when Coke proposed that he should be allowed to reinstate Sir John Turner's bank, the commissioners minuted that very little tidal scour was being provided from the Slade waters except in the case of "forced or raging tides, which very rarely occur". The matter was discussed at a meeting of the commissioners in January 1808 and the proposal accepted partly for this reason, partly because there was seen to be some public benefit in improving the Slade marsh, but principally because Coke undertook to build a tidal reservoir which would provide more water than came off the Slade. This, the commissioners minuted, would "…several times a fortnight return a powerful body of backwater to assist in cleansing the harbour, whereas the Slade is now very seldom in a condition to render any service at all in this respect." They did specify that the reservoir should contain not less than five thousand tons of water. Coke went ahead to cut off the Slade from the harbour creek (although the line of his embankment was not so far forward as that of 1758) but…put not your trust even in great commoners…never went on to complete the reservoir.[6]

NOTES

1 1733-1821. Later Sir James Mansfield and lord chief justice of common pleas.

2 NRO MS486.

3 NRO MS486.

4 NRO MS486.

5 NRO NRS 8723 (21 D1).

6 Tidal Harbours Commission appendix; copy minute of commissioners 29 January 1808 and oral evidence.

5. The nineteenth century; prosperity and decline

There were two ambitious schemes in the early part of the nineteenth century to transform Wells harbour, neither ever proceeding beyond initial proposals. The first of these, in 1804, was a plan by two Norwich surveyors to drain the entire eastern marsh, substituting fresh water brought along the coast from the Stiffkey Brook for the tidal scour to keep the harbour open. The proposers admitted that the works would cost £30,000 but asserted that two unnamed gentleman would be prepared to pay in order to obtain the marshland.[1] The scheme sounds impracticable and certainly not cost effective, even given the sharp rise in land values during the Napoleonic wars, and it did not take place.

In 1828 the commissioners received a proposal from one Benjamin Leak, a surveyor of Holt. His plan was to straighten and confine the outer channel from the Scalph Beacon to the bar by a bank on the western side and another from the beacon eastward to Wells Meals. He was confident that this would produce major improvements. The commissioners having turned his plan down initially as too costly, he offered to undertake it himself for nine hundred pounds down and thereafter four hundred pounds per annum out of which he would pay all maintenance of the harbour and quay and any harbour salaries. In the light of experience of attempts to build training walls out over long stretches of sand or mud to deep water at other harbours his idea of likely costs sounds ludicrously inadequate and he was probably lucky to be turned down again at his second time of asking.[2]

The first known efforts by the commissioners themselves were towards enhancement of the flow of water available from Sluice Creek, the outlet of which had formed Freestone's Sluice of the previous century. This was achieved from 1818 onwards by first blocking off the western outlet into the main channel of the Great East Fleet (by a work known as the Horseshoe Bank) and then similarly blocking off the western ends of the other, smaller creeks also flowing off the eastern marsh into the main channel. Thus the majority of the ebbing water from the East Marsh had to exit via Sluice Creek, while at the same time the series of blockages had the effect of somewhat straightening the line of the eastern shore of the main channel. Thirty years later this was judged by some to have effected a considerable improvement in the depth and ease of navigation of the inner channel but others believed that another result had been the accelerated silting up of the East Marsh itself.[3]

Leak had included as part of his abortive scheme a plan to block off the eastern exits to seawards from the East Marsh by a continuous bank from Wells Meals to the Nass Point so that none of the run-off would escape eastwards. This was a more practical project and one which either then or at some later time was in fact achieved by the commissioners themselves at least to the extent of building banks across the eastern ends of the Great East Fleet and of Stonemeals Creek (the eastern end of the upper harbour channel). The evidence for this is that fifty years later it was reported that both these banks, the Warham and Stiffkey banks, were in serious disrepair.

In 1844 Lord Leicester[4] commissioned a report from a London surveyor James Rendel on the practicality of enclosing and draining the West Marsh. Rendel was of the opinion that the run-off from that area contributed little to scouring the harbour, arriving too early on the tide and too far down the harbour. On the other hand a western embankment to the main channel would not only serve to drain the remaining marsh behind it, but would also straighten the main channel. This would at once benefit the navigation, because straight channels encouraged a faster tide flow, and provide land communication to Holkham Meals and the lifeboat house which would be of great benefit in the event (frequent) of wrecks in the area. The life boat, which had been installed in 1830 by a Norfolk society for lifesaving at sea, was largely useless since without a road it could not be reached in severe weather. Rendel also suggested an eastern bank to the inner channel, linking the existing creek blockages, which would further straighten the channel and act to prevent new gullies diminishing the flow exiting via Sluice Creek. He estimated the cost of all works at just under twelve thousand pounds.[5]

Rendel inspected the harbour again early in 1845 and reported directly to the commissioners, making no reference to his earlier report to Lord Leicester's agent. Again he advocated a western embankment, preferably high enough to enable the West Marsh to be drained, but if that was too expensive, then to three quarter tide level at least. An embankment on this reduced scale would not serve to close off the western fleet entirely, but would help further to straighten the inner channel and prevent it splitting into separate branches. It seems that ships could actually get swept onto the West Marsh given strong east or south winds. All the small gullies in the East Marsh should be kept open (some had been filled in, presumably to assist graziers) and the eastern side of the inner channel should be built up to above high water mark to ensure the maximum discharge via the quays. Like Smeaton before him, Rendel was of the opinion that nothing of value could be done outside the dunes. The forces were too vast. However a mussel bank was building near the entrance and this should not be discouraged as it was helpful in keeping the channel from bending too far to the east. Fishermen were digging into the bank

MAP 5

Section of the 1997 edition of the Ordnance Survey 1:25,000 Explorer series, Sheet 24, revised 1996.

The major changes from all the previous maps reflect the building of the western embankment in 1859 and the associated draining of the West Marsh. The line of the channel inward from the Pool was thus straightened on its western side. The East Marsh appears little changed over two hundred years. The outer channel had reverted at the time of survey to something close to the configuration appearing in Faden's map of the 1790's (Map 3), but this is probably coincidence.

The line of the embankment blocking off Warham Slade is now further to the north than shown on Map 4 although still not quite so far to seaward as that of 1759 (Maps 1 and 2).

Shown here at the actual scale of 1:25,000 or approximately 2½ inches to 1 mile. Reproduced from Ordnance Survey mapping on behalf of the Controller of Her Majesty's Stationery Office © Crown Copyright. MC030632.

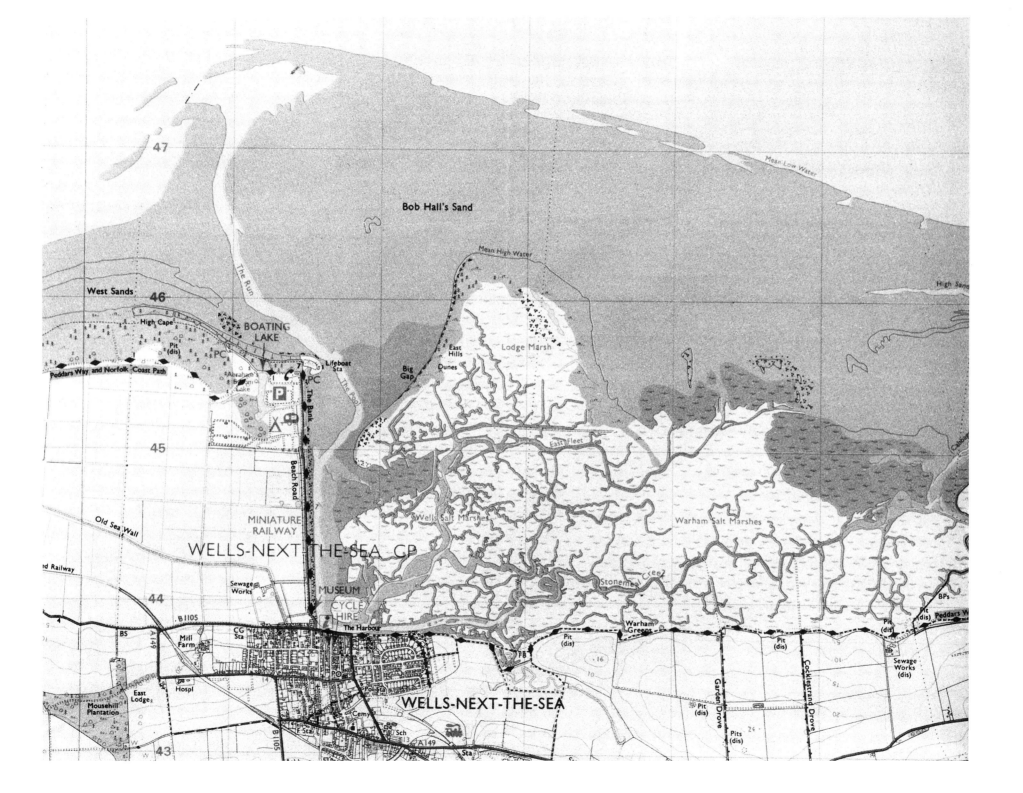

but should be prohibited from doing so for a few years until it had grown further.[6]

In early 1845 the government had set up a royal commission to enquire into the state of all tidal harbours throughout the British Isles. This commission, consisting of a number MPs and naval men (including the famous Hydrographer of the Navy, Francis Beaufort) proceeded in the customary way by sending a lengthy questionnaire to all harbour authorities, following up by holding local hearings. The Wells hearing in October was presided over by Joseph Hume MP, chairman of the commission,[7] who took evidence from local pilots and shipowners as well as from some harbour commissioners. At the hearing the clerk to the harbour commissioners said that he had no harbour maps but produced Rendel's report of February 1845. He held no ancient records, all having been removed under a previous commission and "had not since been heard of." Mr Thomas Garwood, solicitor and agent of Lord Leicester, handed in Rendel's earlier report. At that time Lord Leicester had not made up his mind whether to proceed with the western drainage bank. Garwood understood that the Admiralty were minded to approve, subject to a report by their own engineer.

There was a good deal of local discontent over the exclusive and secretive conduct of the harbour commissioners and their secretary, but this was directed more against their financial dealings than in criticism of the state of the harbour. One of the most vociferous critics was himself a commissioner but it appears that he was also a former harbour master who had been dismissed. Hume was in any case more concerned with financial control and unhealthy concentration of power in the hands of landowners than in navigational matters. The Royal Commission's report runs with appendices to many hundreds of pages covering the whole of the British Isles. The Wells section reads in part:

> The inhabitants struggled for nearly half a century to prevent the enclosure of the tidal lands by the adjoining proprietors, even at the expense of many suits at law; but all these efforts were frustrated, and 846 acres have been enclosed, to the great detriment of the harbour.

> The necessity of supervision of harbours by Government [a major theme of the overall report] further appears from the fact that, under an Act passed so recently as 1844, the sum of £9,650 has been borrowed, on an assignment of the harbour dues, to erect a quay; and the expenditure of this large amount has been left almost entirely under the control of one of the Commissioners, who acts as secretary, collector, treasurer, paymaster, and superintendent …of all public works, and who thus has the whole management of the works and finances, without even the check that would be afforded by the assistance of a clerk or the employment of a practical engineer.

> …the Commissioners named in the Act…many of whom do not even possess any property in the town, have the power of nominating others to fill up vacancies.[8]

Despite the Royal Commission's criticisms of Wells and many other harbours, no major reforms were instituted nationally, nor do there appear to have been any repercussions at Wells. Whether anything was done immediately in pursuance of the Rendel reports is not known. No eastern embankment was ever built, but in March 1857 work was begun on the western embankment.

This was to stretch, as Rendel had hoped, all the way from the western end of the quay to the lifeboat house and the dunes. The *Norfolk Chronicle* recorded the completion of the new "marine promenade" on 12 July 1859. The town, it was reported, was indebted for it to the earl of Leicester (who acquired as a result over five hundreds of acres of new pasture). The length was given as 1 mile 132 yards with a height at maximum of twenty-two feet six inches (presumably from low water mark). Three years later the same paper recorded in December 1862 that the sea had broken through the Wells sandhills and had flooded about 700 acres of the West Marsh, the damage being estimated at ten thousand pounds.[9] At about this time and perhaps in reaction to this flood the dunes were planted with conifers in an attempt to provide some stability.[10] Meanwhile the new promenade, the slightly earlier arrival of the railway from Fakenham and later the coastal railway from Lynn via Heacham put Wells onto the road to becoming the holiday town it is today.

By 1876 the harbour commissioners were in trouble. The channel had silted badly and had become tortuous between the quay and the Pool, a state of affairs put down as ever to a lack of scour. Apparently all the barriers built at the blocked exits of the East Marsh creeks had deteriorated or been swept away entirely, both at the east and west sides. However there was little money in hand. Moreover there were deeper financial and legal problems. The commissioners had power to borrow £1,500 under the 1769 Act which limit was raised to £5,000 under the Act of 1835. The whole of that sum had been borrowed by the issue of Priority Bonds at five per cent interest and these remained outstanding. The Act of 1844 had further increased the borrowing limit and the new powers had been used to raise a further £8,710 on Non-priority Bonds, also at five per cent.[11] Interest was substantially in arrears but the terms of the Acts forbad any expenditure on harbour maintenance until all interest accrued had been paid.

The commissioners were unable to spend money on professional advice and found the Board of Trade, which by then had some national responsibility for harbours, totally unhelpful. In 1877 they obtained a report from a London engineer, Sir John Coode (who apparently worked without a fee) and an estimate of £1,165 from a local man for essential works plus some £5,000 if a half-tide guide wall recommended by Sir John were to be built to straighten the channel. Any expenditure was however out of the question until the financial problems could be solved. This was not achieved until 1882 when the bondholders were persuaded to accept repayment at substantial discounts out of money raised on new bonds. Priority bondholders received fifty per cent of their money and the remainder just fifteen per cent, both sets presumably aware that as their security was the harbour dues there could be nothing gained by seeing the harbour closed altogether. The new bonds on the same security raised £4,520 of which £3,807 was required to pay off the old, leaving a modest balance to effect the most urgent works which were carried out over the next three years. An important feature of the new bonds was that interest at a maximum of five per cent was not cumulative and need be paid for any year only at such rate as the commissioners considered could be afforded. It was this concession that saved the harbour from bankruptcy in later years.

By 1884 the commissioners were able to report a considerable improvement although the works carried out might best be described as patchwork. However by digging out a bank of hard clay in the channel a near miraculous cure had been effected in the inner channel which had both straightened and deepened itself without any need for the proposed training wall. A map of

1884, prepared by a lieutenant of the Royal Engineers (a relation of one of the commissioners) shows not only a straightened inner channel but an alignment of the outer route across the sands very similar to that described as ideal and pertaining in the early eighteenth century. It was reported that "A vessel lying at the quay, as soon as it is afloat, can now proceed to sea." [12]

Nevertheless the trade through the harbour was declining seriously. In the first half of the nineteenth century Wells harbour was certainly busy. Outward corn shipments coastwise between 1819 and 1827, mainly barley, averaged 11,800 tons annually which suggests that the channels must have remained in at least a tolerable state.[13] At some time before 1845 the commissioners had invested in a steam tug which would have been of great assistance in towing sailing vessels in and out of the harbour when winds were adverse. After the 1820s evidence is lacking for the tonnage passing through the harbour but from 1839 there is at first intermittent and then from 1858 continuous information on the level of harbour dues which provides clear evidence of the trend in harbour activities. The figure for 1839 was £800 and that for 1845 £1,007 which may possibly be the highest ever recorded until revised rates were charged in the following century.[14] The average for the ten years to 1869 was £780 (the highest year being 1864 when the total was £939). But thereafter receipts began to fall significantly. The next ten years averaged only £470. In 1884 receipts were £436; in 1894 £232; in 1904 £254; and in 1914 just £140. When it is appreciated that some fifty pounds or more of the receipts in these later years were from oyster or mussel layings it will be obvious that by 1914 commercial traffic through the port was but a shadow of its former self.[15]

The causes of the decline may have included difficulties with the harbour. It is unlikely that the commissioners' concerns in 1879 were not reflected in some trade being lost to other ports although photographs from the 1890s suggest that quite large vessels were still appearing in the harbour. However a major factor must have been the arrival of the railway in 1857. Two years later a line was run around the eastern side of the town to the quay itself. Port receipts may in those years have been buoyed up by the import of materials for railway construction. Perhaps initially commercial prospects seemed bright with the hinterland of the port being so much extended but soon enough the coal trade would have been killed once Midlands coal began to arrive by rail in place of northern coal by ship. The railway would also quickly have replaced shipping as the means of bringing in consumer goods for the retailers of the area. Meanwhile the great agricultural depression, which began in the 1870s and, wartime apart, never truly ceased until the 1940s, must inevitably have served to reduce substantially the trade in grain.

1 Report by Kent & Creasy NRO MS13949.

2 Tidal Harbours Commission appendix; copy of report by Benjamin Leak, 21 March 1828.

3 Tidal Harbours Commission appendix; oral evidence and copy of report by James M Rendel, 6 February 1845

4 Thomas William Coke (1822/1909), second earl of Leicester of the second creation, son of Thomas Coke who near the end of his long life had taken the title of earl of Leicester held formerly by his great uncle in the early eighteenth century.

5 Tidal Harbours Commission appendix; copy of report by James M Rendel, 5 December 1844.

6 Tidal Harbours Commission appendix; copy of report by James M Rendel, 6 February 1845.

7 Joseph Hume (1777/1855) radical politician, in 1845 MP for Montrose in Scotland, itself a tidal harbour of some importance.

8 Tidal Harbours Commission Second Report 20 March 1846, pp.XIV/XV and appendix.

9 Charles Mackie, *Norfolk Annals* Vol 2 (Norwich, 1901).

10 Susanna Wade Martins, *A Great Estate at Work* (Cambridge, 1980) p.131.

11 It is assumed that the sum of £9,650 referred to by the Royal Commission report in 1844 referred to the combined state then of old and new borrowing.

12 Wells Harbour Office; Records of Harbour Commissioners; financial records and printed reports.

13 John Armstrong & Philip S. Bagwell, "Coastal Shipping", in Derek H. Aldcroft & Michael J. Freeman (eds.), *Transport in the Industrial Revolution* (Manchester, 1983) pp.157.

14 Purchas, History, p.54.

15 Wells Harbour Office; Records of Harbour Commissioners; cash books.

6. A final flowering

To judge from the harbour cash books the port was virtually unused during the first World War and in the years immediately after. Yet despite all earlier predictions it was not further silting which caused the port's twentieth century demise as a commercial harbour. The outer channel has never varied materially in depth although it and the inner channel have wandered in their course over the years and continue to do so. That the harbour remained viable for small ships was demonstrated when, after an agreement had been reached between the commissioners and the Yorkshire Sugar Company in 1932, the port was used for the carriage of sugar beet between Norfolk and the Humber. For the few years leading up to the next war the harbour was once again mildly prosperous to the extent that the commissioners were able to pay some interest on the old harbour bonds when scarcely any had been paid in the preceding decade.

The second World War destroyed the beet trade and all other trading through the port, air-sea rescue being the chief harbour activity during the war years. Nor did trade swiftly recover after the war was over. The disastrous floods of 1953 broke through all the seawalls and flooded all the drained marshes right up to the old staithe by the church. Following this and another severe flood in 1978 the seawalls have been rebuilt by the authorities responsible for flood defences to greater heights than ever but, while the harbour commissioners have repaired the quay, their expenditure on the harbour itself has been confined mainly to the replacement and lighting of buoys and beacons and some minor channel dredging, these in part paid for by government grants. Other dredging has been carried out for extraction of gravel and sand rather than in aid of the navigation. However from the early 1970s and through to 1988 there was a late flowering of commercial shipping through the port, the volumes of which exceeded by far the throughput of the most prosperous times of the previous century.

During this period the port was receiving at the height of the revived trade as many as 250 diesel driven coasters annually, often Dutch owned, all of less than 500 tons and none drawing more than ten feet or having serious problems lying in the mud by the quay at low tide. These vessels brought up to 100,000 tons of animal feedstuffs, soya beans and fertilisers each year, chartered by small shippers seeking to by-pass union dominated and overpriced larger ports. The end of this latter period of prosperity was due to commercial rather than navigational reasons. New and larger ships were replacing the small coasters, having four or five times their capacity yet running with crews little larger. These ships were not too deep to enter Wells but were too long to turn in the limited space by the quay. At the same time other ports had better landward access and handling facilities while Wells became less competitive in price as new regulations raised the comparative costs of small harbour operation. Today there is no commercial cargo traffic at all.

Why, in the light of the old arguments and in the absence of any major engineering work since 1859, has the harbour not long since been lost altogether as has happened for all but small craft at the other harbours of north Norfolk? The answer in part would seem to be that, unlike Brancaster and Blakeney, it has never in historic times been menaced by any advancing spit. But equally or more important has been the continued tidal access to the whole of the main eastern marsh. No doubt creeks within this area continue to silt but the process is very slow and may be temporarily reversed, the creeks cleaned out, by the effects of storm tides and surges. What may be the effect of a further rise in relative sea level will depend on the speed at which it occurs: the marsh might build yet higher, or it and the dunes might ultimately be swept away altogether. The only certainty is that further change will occur, no more predictable in a timescale of human lifespans than it has been in the past.

AERIAL VIEW

Aerial view of the harbour looking eastwards over the quay and along the harbour creek. Sluice Creek, now full of yacht moorings, is to the left and in the far distance is the blocked entrance to Warham Slade.